Sing & Learn
Times Tables

Multiplication is the name of the game.
Soon you'll be able to say, 'See ya later calculator!'

$9 \times 11 =$ $8 \times 5 =$

$2 \times 8 =$ $7 \times 6 =$ $12 \times 3 =$

Contents

Introduction

The purpose of this activity book is to teach, reinforce and practise the times tables in a stimulating and fun way. The activity book used in conjunction with the sing-along CD will enhance mastery of the times tables. These activities can be used to assist students to develop an understanding of number patterns, number order, multiplication processes and number word recognition.

The book is organised in order, from the two times to the twelve times table. Revision activities are included for additional practice and reinforcement of tables previously introduced. Answer pages are provided at the back of the book to aid self-correction. Reward stickers are used after each set of table activities to promote motivation and enjoyment. They can be placed on the certificate page at the end of the book.

This activity book is targeted towards middle primary students or older students who have difficulty learning tables. These activities have been compiled by two primary teachers who saw a need to present tables in a variety of ways that would be enjoyable for students as well as educational.

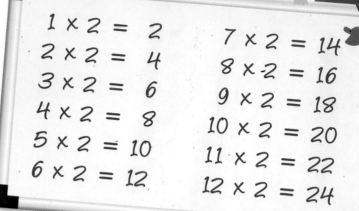

1 × 2 = 2		7 × 2 = 14
2 × 2 = 4		8 × 2 = 16
3 × 2 = 6		9 × 2 = 18
4 × 2 = 8		10 × 2 = 20
5 × 2 = 10		11 × 2 = 22
6 × 2 = 12		12 × 2 = 24

Get your pen ready!

 Play the CD. Now you're ready to listen to the 2 times table!

TASK 1

Circle the answers on the grid as you listen.

1	2	3	4	5	6	7	8	9	10
11	12	13	14	15	16	17	18	19	20
21	22	23	24	25	26	27	28	29	30

TASK 2

Can you help the dogs find their bones?
Draw a line from the bone to the correct dog.

3x2=   12x2=   8x2=   6x2=   7x2=
10x2=   5x2=   2x2=   11x2=

16   22   20   4
12   6   24
10   14

4

TASK 3

Count the dog bowls by making groups of 2. Then make the table sum by filling in the boxes.

Count by twos.

$\bigcirc$ x $\bigcirc$ = $\bigcirc$

TASK 4

Break the code. Use the code to find out the type of dog. The first one is done for you.

A	D	B	T	P	E	H	G	L	I	S	R	O
2	12	18	0	8	20	6	16	10	14	22	24	4

2x5	2x1	2x9	2x12	2x1	2x6	2x2	2x12
10							
L							

TASK 5

Find the words. The answers to the tables are hidden in the word find. Look across, down and diagonally. Write in the answer and shade the word on the grid.

There are also two words that mean 2.

h	d	x	s	b	c	n	p
s	i	x	t	e	e	n	a
s	t	w	e	l	v	e	i
o	w	n	n	f	o	u	r
u	o	j	f	o	u	y	m
d	o	u	b	l	e	z	w

8x2=☐   6x2=☐   1x2=☐

3x2=☐   2x2=☐   5x2=☐

Turn to page 30 and check your answers.

Great work!!
Give yourself a sticker.

1 × 3 = 3	7 × 3 = 21
2 × 3 = 6	8 × 3 = 24
3 × 3 = 9	9 × 3 = 27
4 × 3 = 12	10 × 3 = 30
5 × 3 = 15	11 × 3 = 33
6 × 3 = 18	12 × 3 = 36

Get your pen ready!

 Play the CD. Now you're ready to listen to the 3 times table!

TASK 1 — Circle the answers on the grid as you listen.

1	2	3	4	5	6	7	8	9	10
11	12	13	14	15	16	17	18	19	20
21	22	23	24	25	26	27	28	29	30
31	32	33	34	35	36	37	38	39	40

TASK 2 — Guess which room the robot will clean?

15	9	36	24	30	21
M	O	B	R	D	E

Break the code.

3x3	5x3	12x3	8x3	10x3	7x3	3x3

Unjumble the letters to make a word.

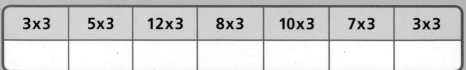

TASK 3

Group the robots in threes and give each group a pencil. We've done the first group for you.

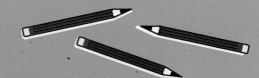

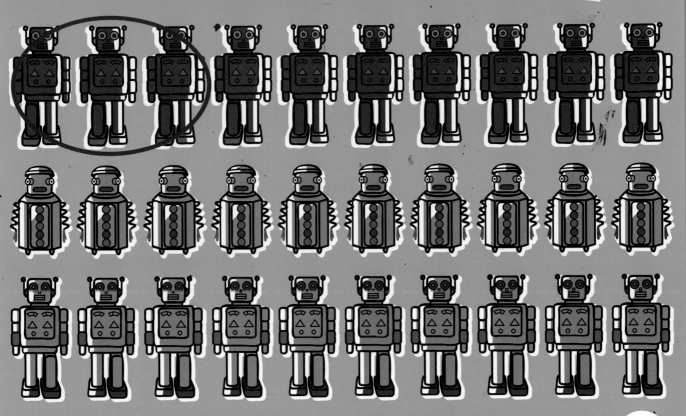

How many pencils altogether? ◯

TASK 4

Program the robot. Write the table to match each button for the robot to do the job.

Cook	21	
Clean	36	
Study	30	
Sing	9	
Play	18	

Turn to page 30 and check your answers.

Well done!!
Give yourself a sticker.

4

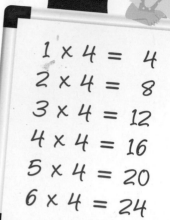

1 x 4 = 4	7 x 4 = 28
2 x 4 = 8	8 x 4 = 32
3 x 4 = 12	9 x 4 = 36
4 x 4 = 16	10 x 4 = 40
5 x 4 = 20	11 x 4 = 44
6 x 4 = 24	12 x 4 = 48

Get your pen ready!

Play the CD. Now you're ready to listen to the 4 times table!

TASK 1 Circle the answers on the grid as you listen.

1	2	3	4	5	6	7	8	9	10
11	12	13	14	15	16	17	18	19	20
21	22	23	24	25	26	27	28	29	30
31	32	33	34	35	36	37	38	39	40
41	42	43	44	45	46	47	48	49	50

TASK 2

Write them in order from smallest to largest on the elephant's trunk.

Circle the numbers in the 4 times table.

TASK 3

Count by fours. Count the peanuts by making groups of 4. Then make the table sum by filling in the boxes.

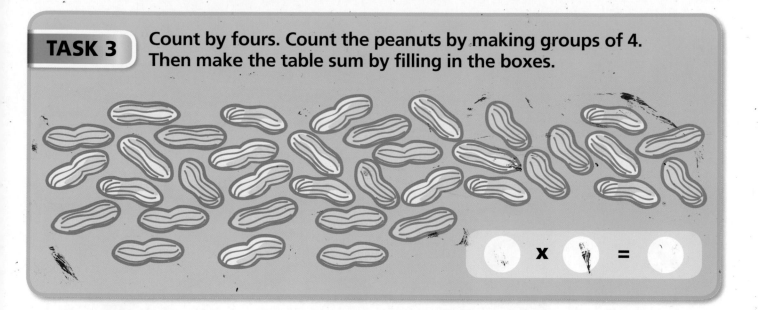

( ) x ( ) = ( )

TASK 4

Ride the elephant. Write the answer to the sum on each ladder step and climb to the top.

36 how many 4s = _____

16 how many 4s = _____

28 how many 4s = _____

40 how many 4s = _____

4 how many 4s = _____

Enjoy your ride!

Turn to page 30 and check your answers.

 Fantastic!!
Give yourself a sticker.

1 × 5 = 5	7 × 5 = 35
2 × 5 = 10	8 × 5 = 40
3 × 5 = 15	9 × 5 = 45
4 × 5 = 20	10 × 5 = 50
5 × 5 = 25	11 × 5 = 55
6 × 5 = 30	12 × 5 = 60

Get your pen ready!

Play the CD. Now you're ready to listen to the 5 times table!

TASK 1   Circle the answers on the grid as you listen.

1	2	3	4	5	6	7	8	9	10
11	12	13	14	15	16	17	18	19	20
21	22	23	24	25	26	27	28	29	30
31	32	33	34	35	36	37	38	39	40
41	42	43	44	45	46	47	48	49	50
51	52	53	54	55	56	57	58	59	60

TASK 2   The babies are hungry. Do the sum and feed them the correct worm.

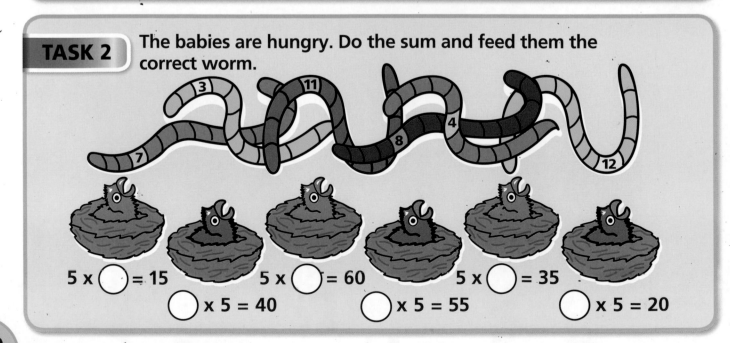

5 x ◯ = 15   5 x ◯ = 60   5 x ◯ = 35

◯ x 5 = 40   ◯ x 5 = 55   ◯ x 5 = 20

TASK 3

Help the parrots fly home. Draw a line from each parrot to its correct nest.

9x5=

5x5=

1x5=

6x5=

11x5=

Nests: 45, 55, 25, 5, 30

TASK 4

Share the parrot's eggs. Draw a line from each egg to a nest.

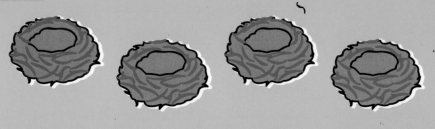

Make sure there are the same amount of eggs in each nest.

How many eggs in each nest?

Turn to page 30 and check your answers.

Hooray!!
Give yourself a sticker.

$1 \times 6 = 6$
$2 \times 6 = 12$
$3 \times 6 = 18$
$4 \times 6 = 24$
$5 \times 6 = 30$
$6 \times 6 = 36$

$7 \times 6 = 42$
$8 \times 6 = 48$
$9 \times 6 = 54$
$10 \times 6 = 60$
$11 \times 6 = 66$
$12 \times 6 = 72$

Get your pen ready!

Play the CD. Now you're ready to listen to the 6 times table!

TASK 1

Circle the answers on the grid as you listen.

1	2	3	4	5	6	7	8	9	10
11	12	13	14	15	16	17	18	19	20
21	22	23	24	25	26	27	28	29	30
31	32	33	34	35	36	37	38	39	40
41	42	43	44	45	46	47	48	49	50
51	52	53	54	55	56	57	58	59	60
61	62	63	64	65	66	67	68	69	70
71	72	73	74	75	76	77	78	79	80

TASK 2

Start at 0 and count by six. Join the dots to form the outline.

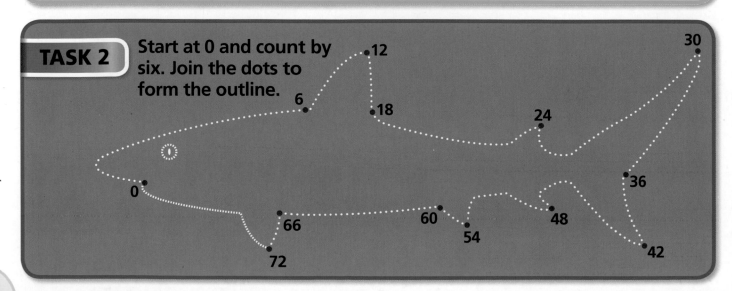

12

Break the code. Fill the boxes and find the name of a shark. The first one is done for you.

R	K	T	A	S	E	I	H	G	W
36	12	72	60	42	30	24	54	6	0

	1x6	6x6	5x6	10x6	12x6	0x6	9x6	4x6	12x6	5x6	7x6	9x6	10x6	6x6	2x6
6															
G															

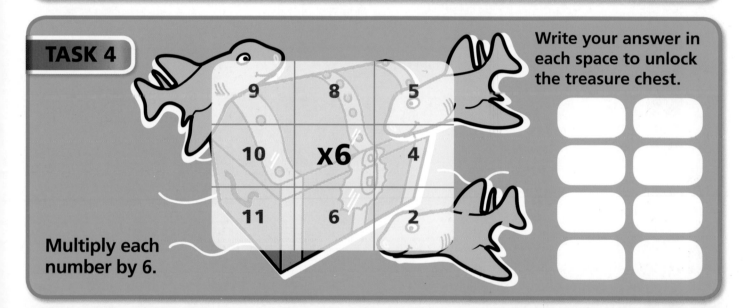

Write your answer in each space to unlock the treasure chest.

9   8   5

10   x6   4

11   6   2

Multiply each number by 6.

Count the sharks. Share the sharks equally between 6 fishermen.

How many did each fisherman catch?

Write the matching table.

◯ x ◯ = ◯

Turn to page 30 and check your answers.

Well caught!!
Give yourself a sticker.

13

7

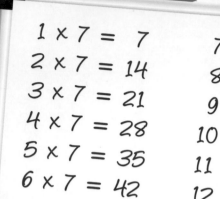

1 x 7 = 7	7 x 7 = 49
2 x 7 = 14	8 x 7 = 56
3 x 7 = 21	9 x 7 = 63
4 x 7 = 28	10 x 7 = 70
5 x 7 = 35	11 x 7 = 77
6 x 7 = 42	12 x 7 = 84

Get your pen ready!

Play the CD. Now you're ready to listen to the 7 times table!

TASK 1   Circle the answers on the grid as you listen.

1	2	3	4	5	6	7	8	9	10
11	12	13	14	15	16	17	18	19	20
21	22	23	24	25	26	27	28	29	30
31	32	33	34	35	36	37	38	39	40
41	42	43	44	45	46	47	48	49	50
51	52	53	54	55	56	57	58	59	60
61	62	63	64	65	66	67	68	69	70
71	72	73	74	75	76	77	78	79	80
81	82	83	84	85	86	87	88	89	90

TASK 2   Write the answers in the boxes to lead Dino home.

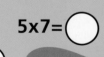

5x7=◯

8x7=◯

6x7=◯

◯ x7=21

◯ x7=63

4x7=◯

◯ x7=84

TASK 3

13
42
15
21
64
63
35
84
71
14

Circle the numbers that match the 7 times table.

TASK 4

Find the 7 times tables hidden in the squares. The x and = signs have been left out. Circle the tables like the one shown.

3	7	21	8	8	7	56
3	10	7	70	9	7	63
27	70	11	7	77	49	36
4	7	28	43	0	7	0
71	83	6	7	42	1	54
2	7	14	1	7	7	41

TASK 5

Draw 3 groups of 7 dinosaur eggs.

How many eggs are there?

Turn to page 30 and check your answers.

Super!!

Give yourself a sticker.

$$1 \times 8 = 8$$
$$2 \times 8 = 16$$
$$3 \times 8 = 24$$
$$4 \times 8 = 32$$
$$5 \times 8 = 40$$
$$6 \times 8 = 48$$

$$7 \times 8 = 56$$
$$8 \times 8 = 64$$
$$9 \times 8 = 72$$
$$10 \times 8 = 80$$
$$11 \times 8 = 88$$
$$12 \times 8 = 96$$

Get your pen ready!

 Play the CD. Now you're ready to listen to the 8 times table!

TASK 1 Circle the answers on the grid as you listen.

1	2	3	4	5	6	7	8	9	10
11	12	13	14	15	16	17	18	19	20
21	22	23	24	25	26	27	28	29	30
31	32	33	34	35	36	37	38	39	40
41	42	43	44	45	46	47	48	49	50
51	52	53	54	55	56	57	58	59	60
61	62	63	64	65	66	67	68	69	70
71	72	73	74	75	76	77	78	79	80
81	82	83	84	85	86	87	88	89	90
91	92	93	94	95	96	97	98	99	100

TASK 2 Fill the gaps.

$$7 \times 8 = \bigcirc$$

$$8 \times \bigcirc = 24$$

$$12 \times 8 = \bigcirc$$

 $$\bigcirc \times 8 = 64$$

  $$\bigcirc \times 8 = 80$$

TASK 3

Circle the shells that are the answer to an eight times table.

96 · 24 · 32 · 28 · 48 · 20 · 80 · 64 · 42 · 8 · 41 · 16

TASK 4

Make octofun table sums by multiplying the 8 with each tentacle number.

Write each sum.

◯ x ◯ = ◯

Turn to page 31 and check your answers.

Incredible!!
Give yourself a sticker.

Get your pen ready!

1 × 9 = 9	7 × 9 = 63
2 × 9 = 18	8 × 9 = 72
3 × 9 = 27	9 × 9 = 81
4 × 9 = 36	10 × 9 = 90
5 × 9 = 45	11 × 9 = 99
6 × 9 = 54	12 × 9 = 108

 Play the CD. Now you're ready to listen to the 9 times table!

TASK 1 Circle the answers on the grid as you listen.

1	2	3	4	5	6	7	8	9	10
11	12	13	14	15	16	17	18	19	20
21	22	23	24	25	26	27	28	29	30
31	32	33	34	35	36	37	38	39	40
41	42	43	44	45	46	47	48	49	50
51	52	53	54	55	56	57	58	59	60
61	62	63	64	65	66	67	68	69	70
71	72	73	74	75	76	77	78	79	80
81	82	83	84	85	86	87	88	89	90
91	92	93	94	95	96	97	98	99	100
101	102	103	104	105	106	107	108	109	110

TASK 2 Dinner time! Draw a line from each sum to the correct answer.

6 × 9 =	3 × 9 =	4 × 9 =.	9 × 9 =	7 × 9 =
sixty-three	eighty-one	fifty-four	thirty-six	twenty-seven

18

TASK 3

Untangle the wool. Follow the string to find the correct answer.

1 x 9 =   8 x 9 =   11 x 9 =   2 x 9 =   5 x 9 =   12 x 9 =

18   99   9   108   72   45

TASK 4

Help the little girl find her lost kitten by counting by 9. Use your pen to draw a path by following numbers in the 9 times table in order.

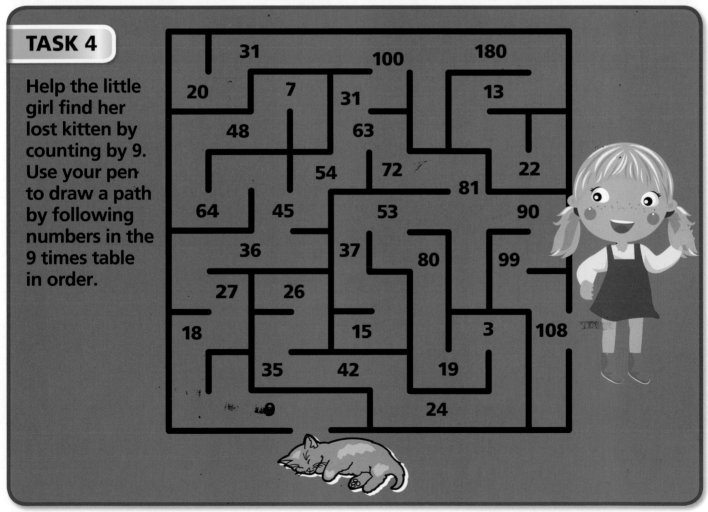

31		100		180
20	7	31		13
48		63		
	54	72		22
64	45	53	81	90
36	37	80	99	
27	26			
18	15	3	108	
35	42	19		
9	24			

Turn to page 31 and check your answers.

Awesome!!
Give yourself a sticker.

10

Get your pen ready!

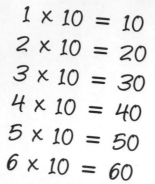

1 × 10 = 10	7 × 10 = 70
2 × 10 = 20	8 × 10 = 80
3 × 10 = 30	9 × 10 = 90
4 × 10 = 40	10 × 10 = 100
5 × 10 = 50	11 × 10 = 110
6 × 10 = 60	12 × 10 = 120

Play the CD. Now you're ready to listen to the 10 times table!

TASK 1 Circle the answers on the grid as you listen.

1	2	3	4	5	6	7	8	9	10
11	12	13	14	15	16	17	18	19	20
21	22	23	24	25	26	27	28	29	30
31	32	33	34	35	36	37	38	39	40
41	42	43	44	45	46	47	48	49	50
51	52	53	54	55	56	57	58	59	60
61	62	63	64	65	66	67	68	69	70
71	72	73	74	75	76	77	78	79	80
81	82	83	84	85	86	87	88	89	90
91	92	93	94	95	96	97	98	99	100
101	102	103	104	105	106	107	108	109	110
111	112	113	114	115	116	117	118	119	120

TASK 2 Solve the puzzle. Brown bear went fishing with his 3 nets. He caught 3 groups of 10 fish. How many fish did he catch altogether?
Write the sum and fill in the correct answer. ◯ X ◯ = ◯

TASK 3

Draw a line to match the correct bear to his honey pot.

4 x 10 =

9 x 10 =

11 x 10 =

8 x 10 =

5 x 10 =

2 x 10 =

fifty   eighty   twenty   ninety   forty   one hundred and ten

TASK 4

Start at 0 and count by ten. Join the dots to form an outline of a bear.

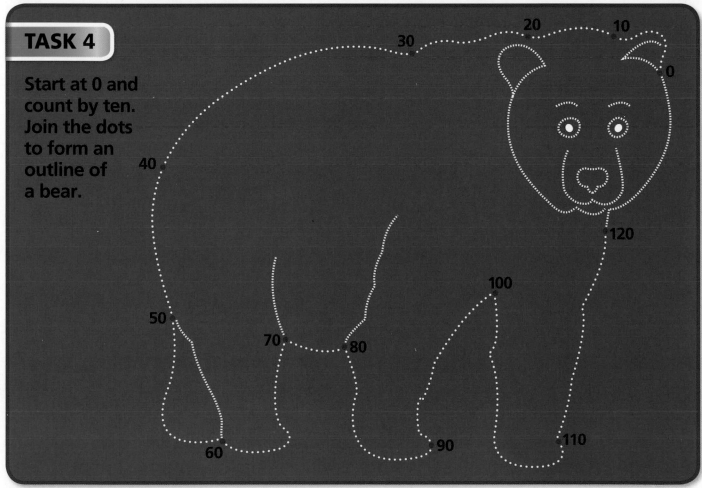

Turn to page 31 and check your answers.

Amazing!!
Give yourself a sticker.

21

$1 \times 11 = 11$
$2 \times 11 = 22$
$3 \times 11 = 33$
$4 \times 11 = 44$
$5 \times 11 = 55$
$6 \times 11 = 66$
$7 \times 11 = 77$
$8 \times 11 = 88$
$9 \times 11 = 99$
$10 \times 11 = 110$
$11 \times 11 = 121$
$12 \times 11 = 132$

Get your pen ready!

Play the CD. Now you're ready to listen to the 11 times table!

TASK 1 Circle the answers on the grid as you listen.

1	2	3	4	5	6	7	8	9	10
11	12	13	14	15	16	17	18	19	20
21	22	23	24	25	26	27	28	29	30
31	32	33	34	35	36	37	38	39	40
41	42	43	44	45	46	47	48	49	50
51	52	53	54	55	56	57	58	59	60
61	62	63	64	65	66	67	68	69	70
71	72	73	74	75	76	77	78	79	80
81	82	83	84	85	86	87	88	89	90
91	92	93	94	95	96	97	98	99	100
101	102	103	104	105	106	107	108	109	110
111	112	113	114	115	116	117	118	119	120
121	122	123	124	125	126	127	128	129	130
131	132	133	134	135	136	137	138	139	140

TASK 2 Order the numbers from lowest to highest.

66   110   99   11   33   88   44   22   0   77   55

__   __   __   __   __   __   __   __   __   __   __

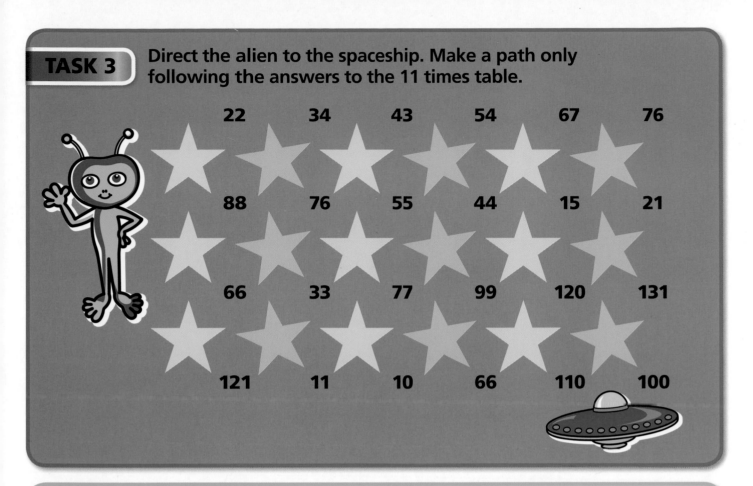

TASK 3 Direct the alien to the spaceship. Make a path only following the answers to the 11 times table.

22	34	43	54	67	76
88	76	55	44	15	21
66	33	77	99	120	131
121	11	10	66	110	100

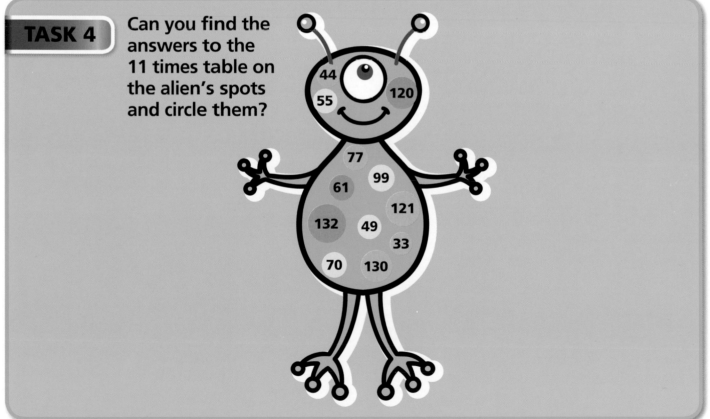

TASK 4 Can you find the answers to the 11 times table on the alien's spots and circle them?

44
55
120
77
99
61
121
132
49
33
70
130

Turn to page 31 and check your answers.

Splendid!!
Give yourself a sticker.

23

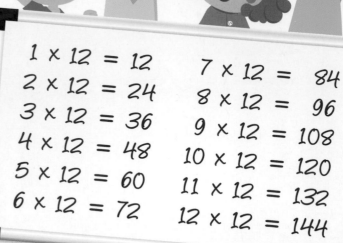

1 × 12 = 12					7 × 12 = 84				
2 × 12 = 24					8 × 12 = 96				
3 × 12 = 36					9 × 12 = 108				
4 × 12 = 48					10 × 12 = 120				
5 × 12 = 60					11 × 12 = 132				
6 × 12 = 72					12 × 12 = 144				

Get your pen ready!

Play the CD. Now you're ready to listen to the 12 times table!

TASK 1 Circle the answers on the grid as you listen.

1	2	3	4	5	6	7	8	9	10
11	12	13	14	15	16	17	18	19	20
21	22	23	24	25	26	27	28	29	30
31	32	33	34	35	36	37	38	39	40
41	42	43	44	45	46	47	48	49	50
51	52	53	54	55	56	57	58	59	60
61	62	63	64	65	66	67	68	69	70
71	72	73	74	75	76	77	78	79	80
81	82	83	84	85	86	87	88	89	90
91	92	93	94	95	96	97	98	99	100
101	102	103	104	105	106	107	108	109	110
111	112	113	114	115	116	117	118	119	120
121	122	123	124	125	126	127	128	129	130
131	132	133	134	135	136	137	138	139	140
141	142	143	144	145	146	147	148	149	150

TASK 2 Complete the sum.
Eight times twelve equals?

◯ x ◯ = ◯

TASK 3

Circle the numbers you would use in the 12 times table.

22   36
12   14
76   108
22   6   84
96
24   72   110
28   92   48
32
98   60
144
120
132

Put them in order from smallest to largest on the line below.

_____

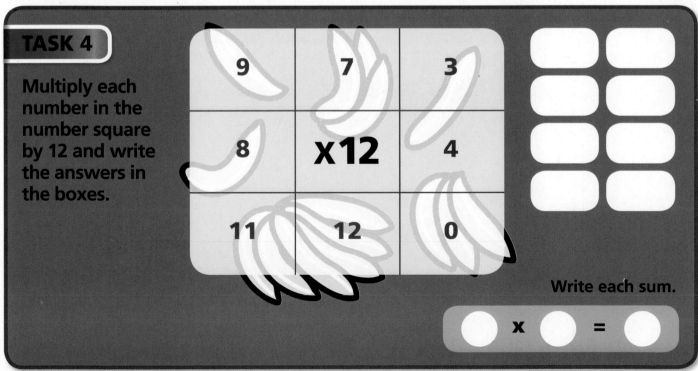

TASK 4

Multiply each number in the number square by 12 and write the answers in the boxes.

9	7	3
8	x12	4
11	12	0

Write each sum.

◯ x ◯ = ◯

Turn to page 31 and check your answers.

Tremendous!!
Give yourself a sticker.

Revision Activities

Table Find

Circle the word answer to each table.

seven x seven =
one x five =
five x six =
two x seven =
eight x five =
ten x five =
eleven x six =

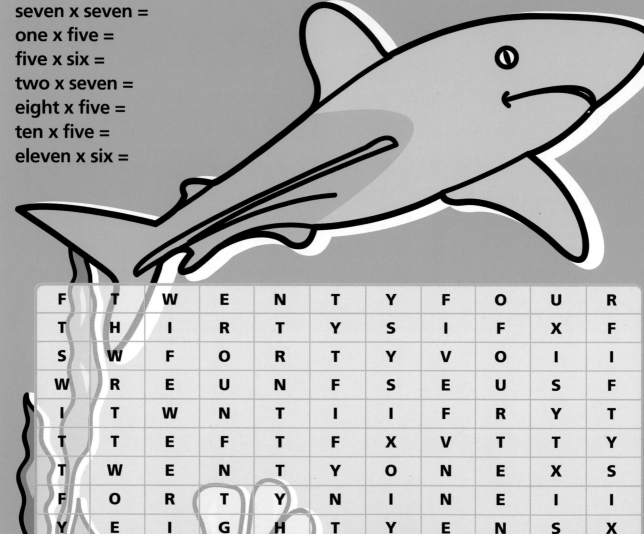

F	T	W	E	N	T	Y	F	O	U	R
T	H	I	R	T	Y	S	I	F	X	F
S	W	F	O	R	T	Y	V	O	I	I
W	R	E	U	N	F	S	E	U	S	F
I	T	W	N	T	I	I	F	R	Y	T
T	T	E	F	T	F	X	V	T	T	Y
T	W	E	N	T	Y	O	N	E	X	S
F	O	R	T	Y	N	I	N	E	I	I
Y	E	I	G	H	T	Y	E	N	S	X

Remember to turn to page 31 and check your answers.

four x six =
eight x seven =
one x six =
four x five =
ten x eight =
three x seven =

Trunks and Bones

Throw the dice and move a counter. If you land on a square with a table, you need to answer it correctly before moving on. If you land on top of an elephant's trunk, you slide down it. If you land at the bottom of a dog's bone, you climb it. The first to get home is the winner.

45	**46** 6x12=	**47**	**48** 5x2=	**Home**
44 4x4=	**43**	**42** 11x4=	**41**	**40** 4x10=
35	**36** 9x3=	**37**	**38** 4x7=	**39**
34 3x4=	**33**	**32** 6x7=	**31**	**30** 0x3=
25 8x2=	**26**	**27** 2x11=	**28**	**29** 6x4=
24	**23** 5x9=	**22**	**21** 12x2=	**20**
15	**16**	**17** 11x3=	**18**	**19** 9x7=
14	**13** 5x4=	**12**	**11**	**10** 7x2=
5 7x3=	**6**	**7**	**8** 12x4=	**9**
4 8x8=	**3**	**2** 5x3=	**1**	**Start**

27

Race Track

Roll the dice and move your counter forward. You must answer the table correctly before you can take your next turn. The first to the finish wins the race!

FINISH

9x12=

Chased by a bear. Go back 2 spaces.

3x9=

5x12=

11x9=

12x12=

12x11=

10x9=

9x11=

6x11=

9x10=

12x9=

3x11=

2x12=

4x10=

1x12=

Take a ride on the bear's back. Move forward 3 spaces.

1x9=

5x9=

7x12=

7x10=

12x10=

8x12=

9x9=

Hit by a coconut. Go back 3 spaces.

11x11=

7x11=

10x10=

6x12=

10x11=

4x11=

Take a banana boost and swing forward 5 spaces.

Alien's spaceship blocking the way. Miss a turn.

6x9=

1x11=

11x12=

11x10=

10x12=

2x10=

4x12=

5x11=

6x10=

4x9=

Zapped by the alien's laser. Go forward 4 spaces.

2x11=

2x9=

3x12=

8x9=

3x10=

1x10=

8x11=

5x10=

3x9=

7x9=

8x10=

START

51

29

Answers

2 Times Table

Task 1 2, 4, 6, 8, 10, 12, 14, 16, 18, 20, 22, 24

Task 2 3x2=6, 10x2=20, 12x2=24, 5x2=10, 8x2=16, 2x2=4, 6x2=12, 11x2=22, 7x2=14

Task 3 4x2=8

Task 4

2x5	2x1	2x9	2x12	2x1	2x6	2x2	2x12
10	2	18	24	2	12	4	24
L	A	B	R	A	D	O	R

Task 5 8x2=16, 3x2=6, 6x2=12, 2x2=4, 1x2=2, 5x2=10

h	d	x	s	b	c	n	p
s	i	x	t	e	e	n	a
s	t	w	e	l	v	e	i
o	w	n	n	f	o	u	r
u	o	j	f	o	u	y	m
d	o	u	b	l	e	z	w

Two words that mean 2 – double & pair

3 Times Table

Task 1 3, 6, 9, 12, 15, 18, 21, 24, 27, 30, 33, 36

Task 2

3x3	5x3	12x3	8x3	10x3	7x3	3x3
O	M	B	R	D	E	O

BEDROOM

Task 3 10 pencils

Task 4 7x3, 12x3, 10x3, 3x3, 6x3

4 Times Table

Task 1 4, 8, 12, 16, 20, 24, 28, 32, 36, 40, 44, 48

Task 2 4, 8, 16, 24, 28, 32, 36, 48

Task 3 9x4=36

Task 4 9, 4, 7, 10, 1

5 Times Table

Task 1 5, 10, 15, 20, 25, 30, 35, 40, 45, 50, 55, 60

Task 2 3, 8, 12, 11, 7, 4

Task 3 9x5=45, 1x5=5, 11x5=55, 6x5=30, 5x5=25

Task 4 5 eggs in each nest

6 Times Table

Task 1 6, 12, 18, 24, 30, 36, 42, 48, 54, 60, 66, 72

Task 2 Dot to dot

Task 3 GREAT WHITE SHARK

Task 5 3 sharks each 3x6=18

Task 4

54	48	30
60	X6	24
66	36	12

8x6=48, 5x6=30, 4x6=24, 2x6=12, 6x6=36, 11x6=66, 10x6=60, 9x6=54

7 Times Table

Task 1 7, 14, 21, 28, 35, 42, 49, 56, 63, 70, 77, 84

Task 2 28, 12, 56, 9, 35, 42, 3

Task 3 42, 21, 63, 35, 84, 14

Task 5 7 eggs + 7 eggs + 7 eggs = 21 eggs

Task 4

3	7	21	8	8	7	56
3	10	7	70	9	7	63
27	70	11	7	77	49	36
4	7	28	43	0	7	0
71	83	6	7	42	1	54
2	7	14	1	7	7	41

8 Times Table

Task 1	8, 16, 24, 32, 40, 48, 56, 64, 72, 80, 88, 96
Task 2	3, 8, 56, 96, 10
Task 3	96, 48, 24, 64, 32, 80, 8, 16
Task 4	9x8=72, 6x8=48, 3x8=24, 5x8=40, 2x8=16, 7x8=56, 10x8=80, 12x8=96

9 Times Table

Task 1	9, 18, 27, 36, 45, 54, 63, 72, 81, 90, 99, 108
Task 2	6x9=fifty-four, 3x9=twenty-seven, 4x9=thirty-six, 9x9=eighty-one, 7x9=sixty-three
Task 3	1x9=9, 8x9=72, 11x9=99, 2x9=18, 5x9=45, 12x9=108

Task 4

10 Times Table

Task 1	10, 20, 30, 40, 50, 60, 70, 80, 90, 100, 110, 120
Task 2	3x10=30
Task 3	4x10=forty, 9x10=ninety, 11x10=one hundred and ten, 8x10=eighty, 5x10=fifty, 2x10=twenty
Task 4	Dot to dot

11 Times Table

Task 1	11, 22, 33, 44, 55, 66, 77, 88, 99, 110, 121, 132
Task 2	0, 11, 22, 33, 44, 55, 66, 77, 88, 99, 110
Task 4	99, 55, 44, 121, 33, 132, 77

Task 3

12 Times Table

Task 1	12, 24, 36, 48, 60, 72, 84, 96, 108, 120, 132, 144
Task 2	8x12=96
Task 3	12, 24, 36, 48, 60, 72, 84, 96, 108, 120, 132, 144

Task 4

108	84	36
96	**X12**	48
132	144	0

7x12=84, 3x12=36, 4x12=48, 0x12=0, 12x12=144, 11x12=132, 8x12=96, 9x12=108

Revision Activities Table Find

seven x seven = forty-nine
one x five = five
five x six = thirty
two x seven = fourteen
eight x five = forty
ten x five = fifty
eleven x six = sixty-six

four x six = twenty-four
eight x seven = fifty-six
one x six = six
four x five = twenty
ten x eight = eighty
three x seven = twenty-one

Sing & Learn
Times Tables
Certificate

☆ 2 Times Table ☆ 3 Times Table

☆ 4 Times Table ☆ 5 Times Table

☆ 6 Times Table ☆ 7 Times Table

☆ 8 Times Table ☆ 9 Times Table

☆ 10 Times Table ☆ 11 Times Table

☆ 12 Times Table

Congratulations!

_____

Times Tables Champion!

Sing & Learn
Times Tables

4

1 × 4	=	4
2 × 4	=	8
3 × 4	=	12
4 × 4	=	16
5 × 4	=	20
6 × 4	=	24
7 × 4	=	28
8 × 4	=	32
9 × 4	=	36
10 × 4	=	40
11 × 4	=	44
12 × 4	=	48

7

1 × 7	=	7
2 × 7	=	14
3 × 7	=	21
4 × 7	=	28
5 × 7	=	35
6 × 7	=	42
7 × 7	=	49
8 × 7	=	56
9 × 7	=	63
10 × 7	=	70
11 × 7	=	77
12 × 7	=	84

10

1 × 10	=	10
2 × 10	=	20
3 × 10	=	30
4 × 10	=	40
5 × 10	=	50
6 × 10	=	60
7 × 10	=	70
8 × 10	=	80
9 × 10	=	90
10 × 10	=	100
11 × 10	=	110
12 × 10	=	120

12

1 × 12	=	12
2 × 12	=	24
3 × 12	=	36
4 × 12	=	48
5 × 12	=	60
6 × 12	=	72
7 × 12	=	84
8 × 12	=	96
9 × 12	=	108
10 × 12	=	120
11 × 12	=	132
12 × 12	=	144

3

1 × 3	=	3
2 × 3	=	6
3 × 3	=	9
4 × 3	=	12
5 × 3	=	15
6 × 3	=	18
7 × 3	=	21
8 × 3	=	24
9 × 3	=	27
10 × 3	=	30
11 × 3	=	33
12 × 3	=	36

6

1 × 6	=	6
2 × 6	=	12
3 × 6	=	18
4 × 6	=	24
5 × 6	=	30
6 × 6	=	36
7 × 6	=	42
8 × 6	=	48
9 × 6	=	54
10 × 6	=	60
11 × 6	=	66
12 × 6	=	72

9

1 × 9	=	9
2 × 9	=	18
3 × 9	=	27
4 × 9	=	36
5 × 9	=	45
6 × 9	=	54
7 × 9	=	63
8 × 9	=	72
9 × 9	=	81
10 × 9	=	90
11 × 9	=	99
12 × 9	=	108

11

1 × 11	=	11
2 × 11	=	22
3 × 11	=	33
4 × 11	=	44
5 × 11	=	55
6 × 11	=	66
7 × 11	=	77
8 × 11	=	88
9 × 11	=	99
10 × 11	=	110
11 × 11	=	121
12 × 11	=	132

2

1 × 2	=	2
2 × 2	=	4
3 × 2	=	6
4 × 2	=	8
5 × 2	=	10
6 × 2	=	12
7 × 2	=	14
8 × 2	=	16
9 × 2	=	18
10 × 2	=	20
11 × 2	=	22
12 × 2	=	24

5

1 × 5	=	5
2 × 5	=	10
3 × 5	=	15
4 × 5	=	20
5 × 5	=	25
6 × 5	=	30
7 × 5	=	35
8 × 5	=	40
9 × 5	=	45
10 × 5	=	50
11 × 5	=	55
12 × 5	=	60

8

1 × 8	=	8
2 × 8	=	16
3 × 8	=	24
4 × 8	=	32
5 × 8	=	40
6 × 8	=	48
7 × 8	=	56
8 × 8	=	64
9 × 8	=	72
10 × 8	=	80
11 × 8	=	88
12 × 8	=	96